WHY THIS IS AN EASY READER

- This story has been carefully written to keep the young reader's interest high.
- It is told in a simple, open style, with a strong rhythm that adds enjoyment both to reading aloud and silent reading.
- There is a very high percentage of words repeated. It is this skillful repetition which helps the child to read independently. Seeing words again and again, he "practices" the vocabulary he knows, and learns with ease the words that are new.
- Only 141 different words have been used, with plurals and root words counted once.

    63 words—almost one-half of the total vocabulary— are used at least three times.

    Almost one-fourth of the total vocabulary has been used at least six times.

    Some words have been used 10, 12 and 15 times.

ABOUT THIS STORY

- An especially easy-to-read excursion into Everychild's fantasy world, where he dreams of power—"when I grow up." The rhymes make for easier reading and give experience with sound-alike words. The theme can lead into the exploration of some of the real-life jobs that men and women do.

When I Grow Up

Story *by* JEAN BETHELL
Pictures *by* RUTH WOOD
Editorial Consultant: LILIAN MOORE

WONDER BOOKS
A Division of Grosset & Dunlap, Inc.
New York, N.Y. 10010

Introduction

These books are meant to help the young reader discover what a delightful experience reading can be. The stories are such fun that they urge the child to try his new reading skills. They are so easy to read that they will encourage and strengthen him as a reader.

The adult will notice that the sentences aren't too long, the words aren't too hard, and the skillful repetition is like a helping hand. What the child will feel is: "This is a good story—and I can read it myself!"

For some children, the best way to meet these stories may be to hear them read aloud at first. Others, who are better prepared to read on their own, may need a little help in the beginning—help that is best given freely. Youngsters who have more experience in reading alone—whether in first or second or third grade—will have the immediate joy of reading "all by myself."

These books have been planned to help all young readers grow—in their pleasure in books and in their power to read them.

Lilian Moore
Specialist in Reading
Formerly of Division of Instructional Research,
New York City Board of Education

When I grow up,
what will I be?

I'll play a little game
and see.
I'll close my eyes
and count to three.

Oh, look!

That's ME!

9

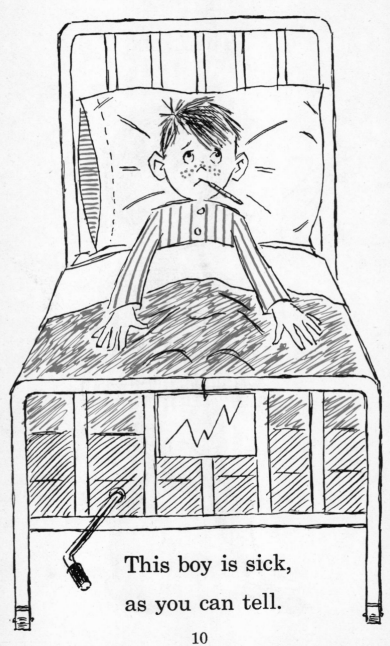

This boy is sick,

as you can tell.

10

Can the doctor
make him well?

The doctor looks
at little Dick.

13

He does not know
why he is sick.

It's all right, Dick.
I know a way
to make you well,
today!

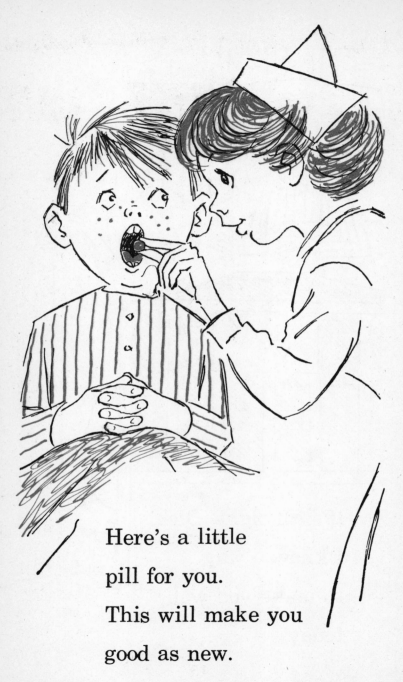

Here's a little
pill for you.
This will make you
good as new.

16

How do you feel?
What do you say?

You're out of bed!

Hooray! Hooray!

18

I like this game.

It's fun to play

and think what I may be

some day.

When I grow up,

what will I be?

I'll close my eyes and see. . .

One, two, three.

Oh, look!

That's ME!

See the horse!

How he can jump!

See that cowboy

go BUMP! BUMP!

Now this cowboy

goes CRASH! CRASH!

And that cowboy
goes SPLASH! SPLASH!

Can I ride him?

I don't know.

I will try.

Here I go!

Will he kick?

Will he jump?

Will I go BUMP! BUMP!

Slow, boy!

Whoa, boy!

And away we go, boy!

I like this game.

It's fun to play

and think what I may be

some day.

When I grow up,

what will I be?

I'll close my eyes and see. . .

One, two, three.

Oh, look!

That's ME!

Do you like to fly?

So do I.

Now we're way up

in the sky.

BANG! POW! Oh, dear!

Something is the matter here.

"We're going down!"
they say to me.
"We will crash
into the sea!"

We will not crash,
for I know how
to fix this plane
RIGHT NOW.

Can I do it?

Nothing to it!

But I must be very quick.
Turn this,
turn that,
turn this. . .
Click, CLICK!

40

41

That is all
I have to do.
Now the plane is
good as new.

I like this game.
It's fun to play
and think what I may be
some day.

When I grow up,

what will I be?

I'll close my eyes and see.

One, two, three.

Oh, look!

That's ME!

Round and round
and round we go.
We are dancing
on one toe!

Now it's time

for all to see

the STAR of the show. . . .

But. . .

Where is she?

Where is the star?

She's very late.

What can we do?

We can not wait.

Someone must do her dance.

Someone must take a chance.

ME?

Oh, my!

All right, I'll try.

Can I do it?

I don't know.

I must do it.

Here I go!

Round and round
and round I go.
See me dancing on one toe!

Are they happy?

Yes, they are.

Hooray! Hooray!

Now I'm the STAR!

I like this game.

It's fun to play

and think what I may be

some day.

What will I do?

What will I be?

When I grow up,

THEN I will see!

CHOOSE FROM THESE EASY READERS